Gerald
Finzi

Romance op 11
for string orchestra

Full score

BOOSEY & HAWKES

Boosey & Hawkes Music Publishers Ltd
www.boosey.com

Published by Boosey & Hawkes Music Publishers Ltd
Aldwych House
71–91 Aldwych
London
WC2B 4HN

www.boosey.com

© Copyright 1952 by Hawkes & Son (London) Ltd

ISMN 979-0-060-12263-7
ISBN 978-1-78454-195-8

New edition: third impression 2016

Printed by Halstan:
Halstan UK, 2–10 Plantation Road, Amersham, Bucks, HP6 6HJ. United Kingdom
Halstan DE, Weißliliengasse 4, 55116 Mainz. Germany

Music origination by Kottamester Bt, Budapest

This work was composed in 1928. It was first performed on 11 October 1951 in Reading, UK, by the Reading String Players, conducted by John Russell.

Recommended recording: Chandos CHAN 9888, by the City of London Sinfonia, conducted by Richard Hickox

Duration: 6 minutes

Performance materials available on hire

to John Russell, musician

ROMANCE
for string orchestra op 11

GERALD FINZI
(1901–56)

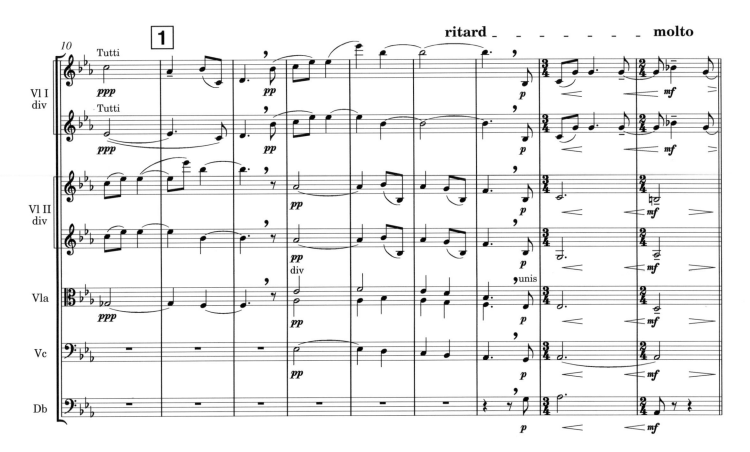

03915

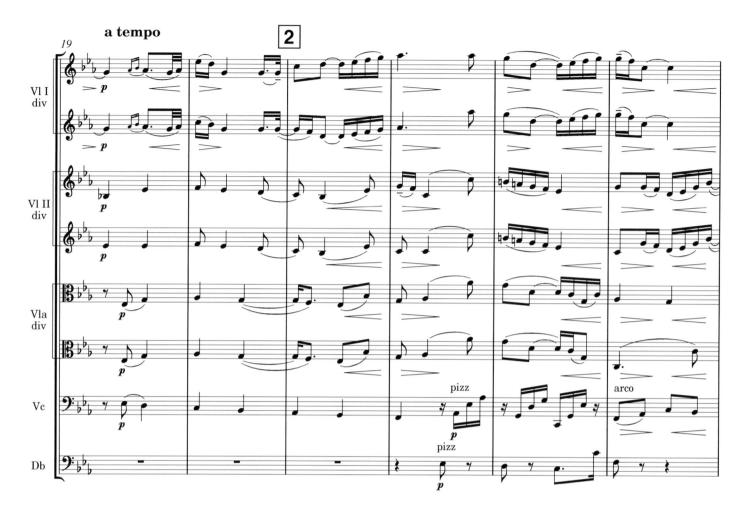

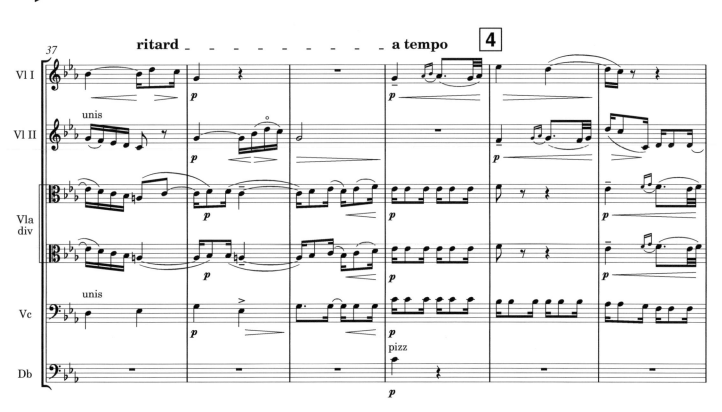

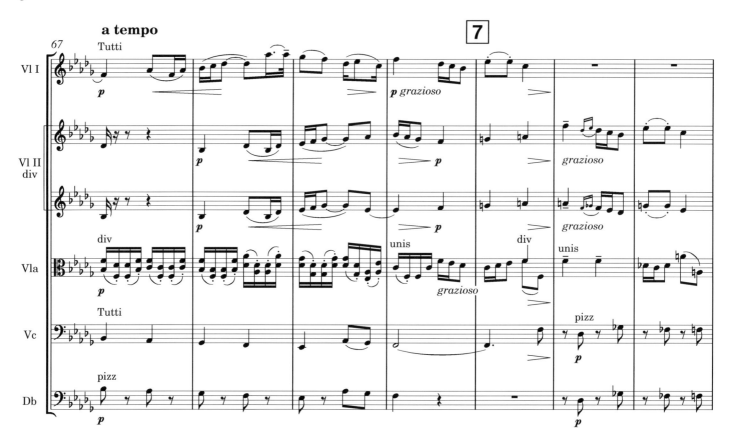

8

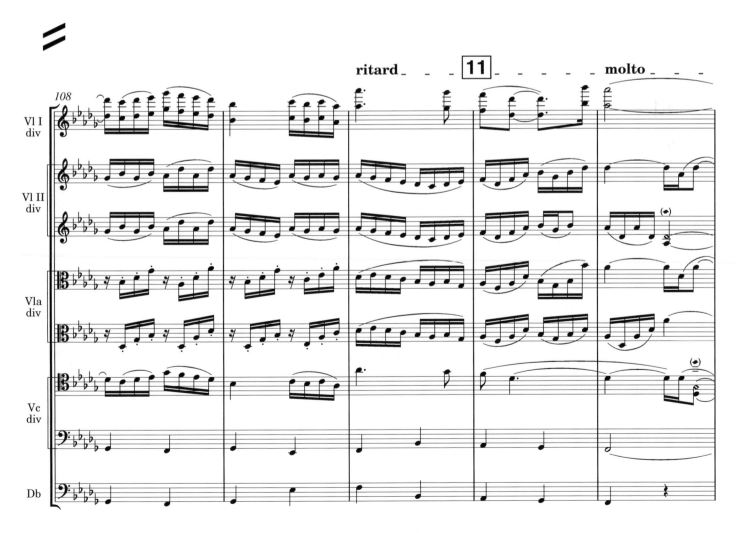